Brainteasers and Puzzles for Kids

ANGUS & ROBERTSON PUBLISHERS

Illustrated by Patrick Cook

P9-CLO-204

Lowdown Logic I

1.

Thirty birds sit on the upper branches of a tree. A so-called 'sportsman' fires three volleys of buckshot at the birds, killing half of one-third of their number.

Can you quickly say how many birds remain?

2.

There are six sandwiches in a brown paper bag. How can you give six hungry young kids a sandwich each and have one left in the bag?

3.

Imagine you have nine cakes and four large paper bags. How can you put an odd number of cakes into each bag without cutting any of the cakes or tearing the bags?

4.

"What day is it?" asked the prisoner suddenly of her cellmate ruminating on the bottom bunk.

"Goodness," replied the other. "Well let's see — the day after the day after tomorrow will be the day before the day before Sunday."

Can you work it out before the short-tempered prisoner lashes out?

5.

How many months have 28 days?

6.

Two fathers and two sons went fishing. Each caught a fish but they landed only three fish in all. How is this possible?

7.

When Mike was first going out with Milly he carved their initials inside a heart on a tree trunk 1 m from the ground. When Mike and Milly were married exactly a year later the tree had grown 20 cm. During the following years it doubled its growth rate annually. How high was the heart on Mike and Milly's tenth wedding anniversary?

Leading Question

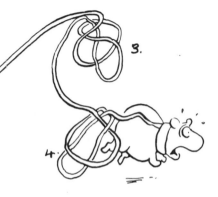

While walking his owner, Robert the bull terrier has managed to tie the lead into many knots. However if he pulled the lead tight some of them might disappear. Under attack from a feral budgerigar he's about to find out which of the knots will stay knotted.

Which knots will not?

Cut the Cube

This 20 cm cube is patterned all over. Pecos William is about to cut it into smaller cubes with 5 cm sides.

Some of the cubes will have 3 patterned faces, some 2, some 1, and some none. How many will there be of each? Help William find out before he is bitten by a maddened bull terrier.

I'll Rephrase That

What are these well-known phrases?

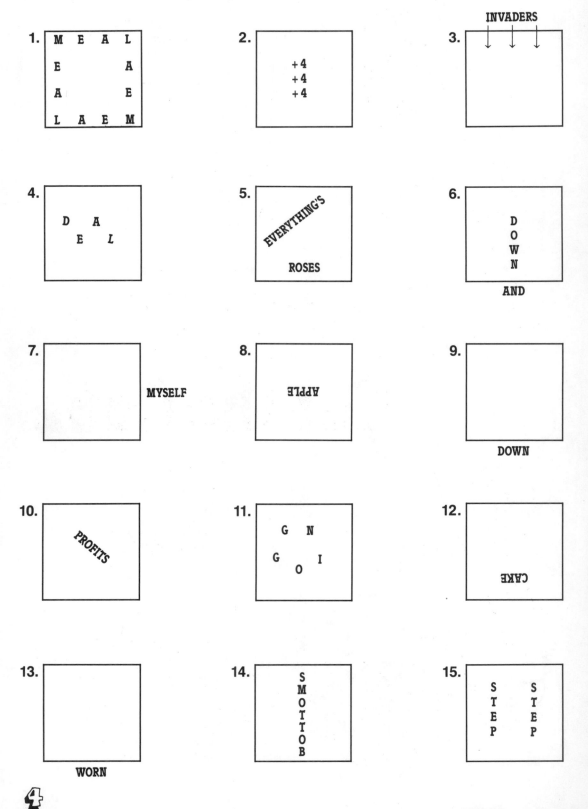

1.
```
M  E    A    L
E            A
A            E
L    A   E    M
```

2.
```
+ 4
+ 4
+ 4
```

3.
INVADERS

4.
```
D     A
   E     L
```

5.
EVERYTHING'S
ROSES

6.
```
D
O
W
N
```
AND

7.
MYSELF

8.
APPLE

9.
DOWN

10.
PROFITS

11.
```
G    N
G        I
   O
```

12.
CAKE

13.
WORN

14.
```
S
M
O
T
T
O
B
```

15.
```
S         S
T         T
E         E
P         P
```

Mirror Mirror

Dame Joan is putting the final touches to her make-up for **The Merry Widow**. Which of the four pictures below shows her face as she sees it in the mirror?

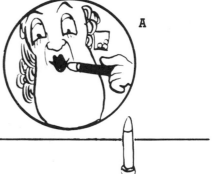

Transformations

Transformations was the name of a parlour game which involved turning one word into another word letter by letter.

For example, here's how to make MILK BOIL:

MILK
MILL
MALL
MAIL
BAIL
BOIL

Now in eight moves turn BLACK into WHITE.

Words Fail Me

1.
Why is the letter 'A' like a flower?

2.
What letter stands for the ocean?

3.
What cat begins with a 'K'?

4.
There is a secret Christmas message in the following letters:

A,B,C,D,E,F,G,H,I,J,K,
M,N,O,P,Q,R,S,T,U,V,W,X,Y,Z

Can you find it?

5.
Why is the letter 'K' like a pig's tail?

6.
Can you spell great joy with three letters?

7.
What time of day is the same, whether it's spelt backwards or forwards or upside down?

8.
Which is right: "The yolk of an egg are white" or "The yolk of an egg is white"?

9.
How do you spell 'we' with two letters without using the letters W and E?

10.
Can you read the following?

Y Y U R Y Y U B
I C U R Y Y 4 ME

11.
What is the difference between here and there?

12.
When Adam introduced himself to Eve, what three words did he use which read the same backwards and forwards?

13.
How do you spell a hated opponent with three letters?

14.
What biblical character is named here:

J
AH

15.
How do you spell boring with three letters?

16.
And now spell wary in two letters.

17.
What common word is this:

B
E

18.
What seven-letter name has only three letters?

19.
How do you spell study with three letters?

20.
What vegetable is this?

C SP H

Q: What do you call a budgie with a tommy gun?
A: Sir.

Something's Fishy!

Chaos reigns in this picture. Something is indeed very fishy. Careful examination will reveal some of the inconsistencies and absurdities but can you find a total of nineteen things wrong with this suburban scene?

Riddle-Me-Ree

Some of the earliest brainteasers were riddles which, in Victorian times, were often in verse. Here is a collection of old-fashioned riddles to test your mettle — are you as astute as your ancestors?

1.
When can you jump over three men without getting up?

2.
In marble walls as white as milk
Lined with skin as soft as silk
Within a fountain crystal clear,
A golden apple doth appear.
No doors there are to this stronghold —
Yet thieves break in and steal the gold.

3.
What can go up a chimney down but can't come down a chimney up?

4.
You use it between your head and toes,
The more it works the thinner it grows.

5.
There was a man who was not born,
His father was not before him,
He did not live, he did not die,
And his epitaph is not o'er him.
    Who was he?

6.
Women don't have it and don't want it.
Men get it, think it's a good thing but they often try to get rid of it.
    What is it?

7.
What is that which has form without substance and size without weight?

Imagine That!

Imagine that you have a single sheet of paper and that you fold it in the middle. Imagine that you fold it again in the middle but in a direction at right angles to the first fold. You now have four thicknesses of paper. Imagine that you cut through the four thicknesses right down the middle of the paper, the cut being parallel with the first fold. How many pieces of paper will you have? How many pieces if the cut is parallel with the second fold?

Diregrams

1.
Draw this envelope in one continuous line without crossing or re-tracing a line or lifting your pencil from the paper.

2.
This is an unusual hoopla. If you can throw just three hoops and separate all seven prizes you win a prize. Just to start you off your first hoop has fallen thus:

3.
Draw this triangular figure in a continuous line, without crossing a line, re-tracing a line or lifting your pencil from the paper.

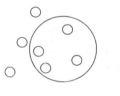

4.
Can you draw this circle and dot without lifting your pencil from the paper? Obviously there's a trick to it, but what?

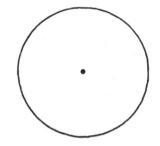

5.
There is no trickery involved with this puzzle. Draw this figure in a continuous line, without lifting the pencil from the paper, crossing a line or re-tracing a line.

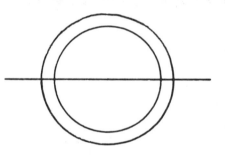

It's Dicey

Which of the dice below could be made from this unfolded one?

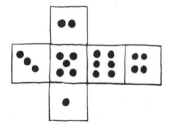

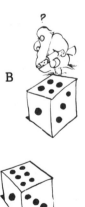

A

B

C

D

Sleeping on the Job

These railway workers are busily laying sleepers. In the following diagram you can see how much is completed and how much remains to be done. How do the two distances compare?

Oh No, Not Maths!

1.
If all even numbers are green and all odd numbers are red what colour is an even number plus an odd number?

2.
There were 99 people on a boat. It turned over. How many were left?

3.
How many spaces are there between the spokes of two 8-spoked bicycle wheels?

4.
If 5 cats catch 5 rats in 5 minutes, how many cats will it require to catch 100 rats in 100 minutes?

5.
What Roman numeral can climb a wall?

6.
Greedy Kate has cut a big cake into slices — a large one for herself and several smaller ones for the rest of the family. Three-quarters of the number of slices to the left of the big slice is 6.

How many slices are there altogether?

7.
How can you make 7 even?

8.
From what number can you take half and leave nothing?

9.
If you count 20 houses on your right going to school, and 20 houses on your left coming home, how many houses in all have you counted?

10.
How are 2 + 2 = 5 and your left hand alike?

11.
How can you remove one-third of six and get nine?

12.
In the ping-pong singles championships semi-finalists Jess, James, Jill and Justin all had to play each other once. How many matches were played altogether?

13.
If a boy took 3 minutes to wash his face, 6 minutes to wash his hands, what would he take to dry them?

14.
Hiram B. Topworthy invented the square phonograph record in a year that reads the same when turned upside down.

Exactly 80 years later in a year with the same peculiarity his son Hiram B. II invented the square harp.

In what year did these musical treats occur?

15.
Molly's big sister is trying to get a share of her birthday party jelly beans.

"Put some in my pockets," she said. "One in the first pocket, 2 in the second, 4 in the third, and so on — doubling the number for each pocket.

"I have 3 pockets in my jeans and 3 in my jacket."

How many jelly beans was she expecting Molly to give her?

16.
Some sexy soubrettes each assisted by their mothers, the serious sultanas, have between them spun and sewn you a silk suit. The work has taken 6 months and in thanks you must salaam each of the sultanas while each sexy soubrette salaams each other soubrette once. There are 36 salaams in all.

How much longer would the work have taken had the serious sultanas not taken part?

17.
Patrick is hopeless at maths but good with figures. He's worked out that 8 nines equal 1125 and proved to his maths teacher that he's right. How did he do it?

18.
Patrick's second effort was to prove that 5 fives are 31. Could he be right again?

19.
What are the next three letters in this sequence?

OTTFFSS _ _ _

Worth a Try?

Waiting on the sidelines are the reserve members of the Cardiff Juniors' Rugby Club. The numbers on their shirts form a series. What number should the reserve wing on the end be sporting?

And what number should he have on the back of his shirt?

Strange Relations

1.

Margery Appleton is looking at a photo of a man. She then says to her father, "That man's mother was my mother's mother-in-law."

Who was in the photograph?

2.

"Here's an astonishing thing," a teacher told his class.

"These two boys were born at the same hour on the same day in the same hospital. They even have the same mother and father and look extraordinarily alike.

"Yet they are not twins . . . and not adopted.

"How could this be?"

3.

What relation is a doormat to a doorstep?

4.

A blind beggar of Paris had a brother that died. The brother that died had no brother. What relation was the blind beggar of Paris to the brother that died?

5.

Maxwell Brown has a robust family of sons and daughters. Each of his daughters has an equal number of brothers and sisters, but each son has twice as many sisters as brothers. How many sons and daughters does Maxwell have?

6.

A certain man once impersonated a country lawyer for a few days.

Before he had been in the office an hour, a very agitated young lady was shown in and said she would like to ask him a question. The impostor tried to look as intelligent as he could, and said, "Certainly! What is it?"

"I want to know," explained the lady, "whether it is permissible for a man to marry his widow's sister?"

If you were in the impostor's shoes, what would you say?

7.

A father and his son were involved in a terrible road accident and both were rushed to hospital unconscious and critically hurt.

"Send the youngster into the operating room first," said the casualty doctor. But, on seeing the lad the surgeon said:

"I can't operate on him. He's my son."

Please explain.

8.

What did John the Baptist and Attila the Hun have in common?

Which Map?

Shown this picture of a country town and asked to draw a map of it, the sixth form geography class set to work. Only one got it right. Was it Tiger, Mouse, Specs or Shirl?

Card Tricks Without Cards

1.

Here is an apparently magic but reasonably simple trick to play on friends.

Ask a friend to think of a card. When he (or she) has done so ask him to multiply it by ten. For multiplication purposes the aces are valued as 1, the jacks, queens and kings are 11, 12 and 13 respectively.

Once he's done as requested ask him to multiply the number he now has by three. Once this has been done tell him:

If the card was a club add 1 to the total he has in mind.

If the card was a heart add 2 to the total he has in mind.

If the card was a spade add 3 to the total he has in mind.

If the card was a diamond add 4 to the total he has in mind.

Now ask him to double the number he is thinking of. If you now ask the person to tell you the total number you can immediately tell him the card he has in mind.

As an example, imagine that the 2 of clubs has been chosen.

2 x 10 = 20
20 x 3 = 60
60 + 1 (for clubs) = 61
61 x 2 = 122

It is now possible to identify the card by the following procedure:

Divide the total by 2 — 122 ÷ 2 = 61.

The last digit tells you the suit, in this case 1 indicates a club. The first digit is then divided by 3 giving you 2, and thus the card is the 2 of clubs.

Try it with other suits and numbers. For example the 9 of hearts.

9 x 10 = 90
90 x 3 = 270
270 + 2 = 272
272 x 2 = 544

Remember, when you have the total, immediately halve it. Of the number that is left, whether it has two or three digits, the last digit gives you the suit and the first or first two digits divided by three will give the card's value.

2.

There are three playing cards in a row. A diamond is on the left of a spade (not necessarily next to it); an 8 is on the right of a king; a 10 is on the left of a heart; a heart is on the left of a spade. What are the three cards?

How Many Triangles?

This tranquil scene contains many triangles. How many can you find?

Oddly Enough

All but one of these drawings have something in common.

Which of them is the odd one out and why?

3.

5.

2.

4.

1.

Lowdown Logic II

1.

During a game of hide-and-seek at Jake's fifth birthday party some of the children hid behind a row of seven trees. Can you work out the smallest possible number of children hidden there from the following clues?

  a A boy is hiding on the right of a girl.
  b A girl is hiding on the right of a girl.
  c Two girls are hiding on the left of a boy.

2.

One of Mabel's three children has taken a slice out of the cake she specially baked to take to the school fete. When questioned they replied as follows:

Bobby: "I didn't."
Susan: "Bobby did it."
Zoe: "Susan is lying."

  Only one of them is telling the truth. The other two are lying. Who stole the cake?

3.

If yesterday's tomorrow was Thursday, what day is the day after tomorrow's yesterday?

4.

Jessie has six red woollen gloves and six green woollen gloves all mixed up in her drawer. Jessie hates waking up in the morning and usually gets dressed with her eyes still shut.

  What is the smallest number of gloves Jessie has to pull out to be certain of getting a pair?

5.

A cross-country skier is caught in a blizzard. Almost frozen, he remembers a shelter shack nearby and stumbles his way towards it, finally making it and crawling through the door. The shack is extremely cold but a fire is laid all ready to be lit. The skier looks at the fireplace, at the oil lamp filled with oil, at the candle in its holder, and then twice at the single match that stands between him and death from freezing. Which shall he light first?

Seeing Things

A windy day at the beach. Without measuring, can you say whose sunshade has the longest handle — Sam's or Sarah's?

Coining It

1.
Set out 10 coins as shown:

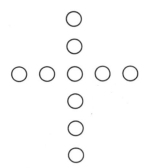

Now by moving just 1 coin (not removing it) turn the pattern into a regular cross with 6 coins in each row.

2.
Arrange 10 coins like bowling pins as shown.

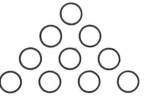

Move just 3 coins and reverse the figure so that the apex is at the bottom.

3.
Arrange 10 coins so as to form 5 lines of 4 coins each.

4.
Stand a coin on its edge, on a table top, and roll it to the left. Does the coin roll clockwise or anticlockwise?

5.
Place 5 coins, three large and two small, in a row with each coin touching the next one, and with the large and small coins alternating.

If we call the large coins **A, B** and **C** and the small coins **a** and **b,** the arrangement will look like this.

$$A \quad a \quad B \quad b \quad C$$

Now in 3 moves shifting 2 touching coins on each move, leave the coins so that the three large ones will be at one end of the line and the two small ones at the other.

Skulduggery

You may win yourself many bets with the following piece of hocus pocus.

Offer to bet a friend, whose age and phone number you don't know, that you can tell him how old he is if he gives you his phone number.

He'll scoff and say it can't be done and it's then you subtly apply the pressure by offering to tell him his age **and** his phone number.

He can't resist — the bets are laid.

You then ask him to do the following on a calculator, with pencil and paper or in his head. Stress that you don't want to know any of the figures but the last.

1. Multiply his phone number by 2.
2. Add 5 to the total.
3. Multiply that total by 50.
4. Add to it his age and the number of days in a year (365).
5. Subtract 615 and what's the total? "887,223,315".

"So you're 15 and your phone number is 887 2233," you'll say.

"Incredible, here's your money" or "I'll have your maths homework done for you in the morning," he'll say.

Try it with your own age and number. Bet it works!

Snails' Pace

These two snails have been asked to take a short cut along the dotted line. If they both move at exactly the same pace, which will reach its destination first?

The Animals Went in Two by Threes

There was merry mayhem one day when 6 emus, 4 roos, a possum, 4 koalas, 3 wombats and 2 echidnas escaped from the Australian section at the zoo. But, on each of the two following days half of the escapees were recaptured.

How many were still free at the beginning of the third day?

How Many Squares?

How many squares can you find in this modern painting?

BIRDCAGE 1

Match Magic

1.
Place 12 matches as shown below.

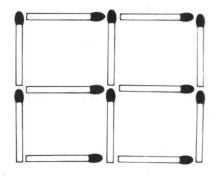

Use this arrangement as a starting point for each of the following:

a   Move 2 matches and make 7 squares.

b   Remove 2 matches and leave 2 squares.

c   Move 3 matches and leave only 3 squares.

d   Remove 3 matches and move 2 to form 3 squares.

e   Move 4 matches and form 3 squares.

f   Remove 1 match and move 4 to make 11 squares.

2.
With a deft touch you can make these 3 matches into 6 without breaking or splitting them.

3.
Add 5 matches to the 6 below to make 9 and prove the mathematicians wrong.

4.
Move 4 matches so that exactly 3 equilateral triangles are formed.

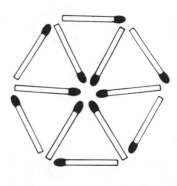

5.
From this row of 7 matches remove 1 match and move 2 so that nothing is left.

6.

Add 8 matches so as to divide this figure into 4 parts of equal size and shape.

7.

Here's a simple two-handed party game with matches. Choose an opponent and lay out 15 matches. You and your opponent take it in turn to take away 1, 2 or 3 matches at a time, the loser being the player who is forced to take the last match.

To be sure to win you must leave 13 matches, then 9, then 5 for your opponent to pick from.

8.

Move just 3 matches in this figure to leave 4 squares.

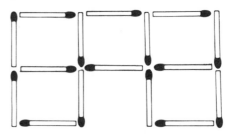

9.

By moving only 3 matches can you make the fish swim in the opposite direction?

Paper Circles Puzzler

For this you will need three long strips of paper about 8 cm wide and 1 m long. Newspaper will do and the following preparation should be done out of sight of your audience.

Take one strip and stick the two ends together.

With the second strip, before sticking the ends together, turn one end of the paper over.

With the third strip, give a double twist before sticking the ends together.

You now have three large circles. The larger the circumference of these circles the better because the twists should not be apparent to the audience.

To present the trick you demonstrate by picking up the first circle (without twists), inserting the point of scissor blades through the paper and cutting in a continuous line around the circle until you have cut it into two complete and separate circles.

Now choose two people from the audience and offer a prize to the one who can duplicate most neatly what you have done.

The person with the second circle (one twist) will end up with one long loop while the one with the third circle (two twists) will achieve two circles but they will be linked.

Magically, neither will qualify for the prize.

Trick Question

Does Gladys use the same pole or poles of different length when performing her two daring tricks?

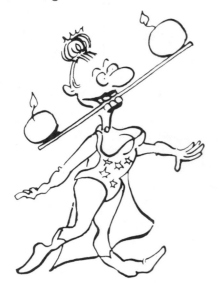

Which Comes Next?

Here is a series of faces. Which of the faces in the row below should come next in the series?

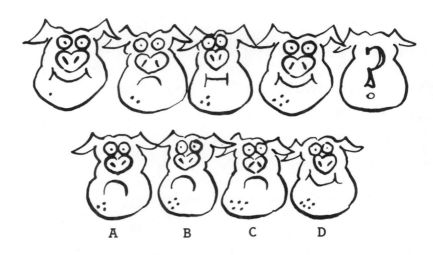

A   B   C   D

What's Odd?

Which of these is the odd one out and why?

A

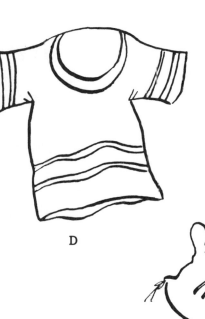

D

C

B

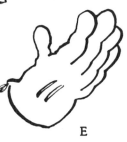

E

Cross Words?

1	2	3	4	5
6				
7				
8				
9				

ACROSS

1. A British magazine

6. A tool

7. A blow

8. A drink

9. A puppet

DOWN

1. Vegetables

2. Sheep

3. Chickens

4. Oceans

5. Often dropped

Lowdown Logic III

1.

An innkeeper had a sudden group of unexpected guests, 11 arriving in one party and demanding beds.

Now the host had only 10 beds at his disposal, but nevertheless, he managed to accommodate them as follows:

He put two in the first bed, but with the understanding that the second should shortly have a bed to himself. He then put the third in the second bed, the fourth in the third bed, and so on, the tenth guest being accommodated in the ninth bed.

He thus had one bed left, into which he now put the eleventh man, who was temporarily sharing the first bed.

Where is the error in the innkeeper's arrangement?

2.

In an antique shop a collector is offered an old lamp with "108 BC" engraved on it. How would he know it was not genuine?

3.

Two workmen were repairing a roof. They fell through a large chimney and landed in the fireplace below.

Now it happened that one man's face was well smeared with soot from his passage through the chimney. The other man's face, however, was absolutely clean. Neither man spoke.

Yet the man with the clean face went and washed his face, the man with the dirty face went back to work without washing his face.

Can you explain, logically, why they did this?

4.

A man who has two sons, each the owner of a horse, dies. His will states that his wealth is to go to the son owning the slower horse of the two. To determine which is the slower, the horses are to be raced between two certain towns. The race begins, and soon becomes a farce, as each brother wants to ride slower than the other. Half way they stop for lunch. A wise old man hears them discussing their difficulty, and when the meal is over, calls each one in turn, and whispers a suggestion to him. The brothers think his idea is a good one, and soon after are seen galloping their hardest. The race is soon over and the one whose horse lost received the legacy.

The words whispered by the old man to each one were the same; what were they?

5.

Mr Duffy meets in the street a friend whom he had once known very well, but of whom he had heard nothing for many years. After greetings had been exchanged, Mr Duffy's friend says: "I have been married since I last saw you, and this is our little daughter."

Duffy asks the little girl her name, and she replies, obstinately: "It's the same as my mother's."

"Oh, then it's Margaret," says Duffy.

"Yes!" she replies.

How did Duffy know the little girl's mother's name was Margaret?

Q: What do you call a cat who has swallowed a duck?
A: A duck-filled fatty puss.

Doodlegrams

Scenes from everyday life? Can you
identify them?

1.

2.

3.
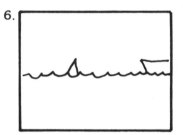

4.
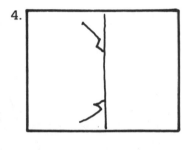

5.

6.
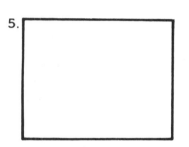

7.
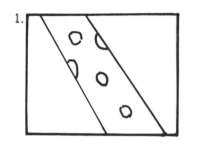

8.
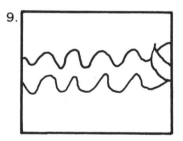

9.
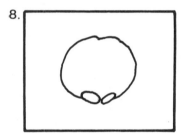

10.
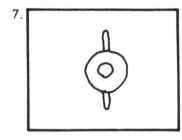

11.
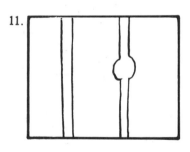

12.
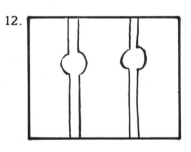

13.
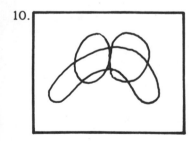

14.
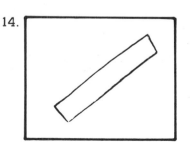

15.
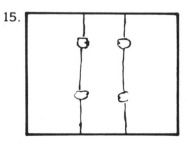

Bound for Botany Bay

There is a route by which convict No. 11973450 can sneak through the ship to the open porthole and freedom. Give him a hand — he's not much of a puzzle solver.

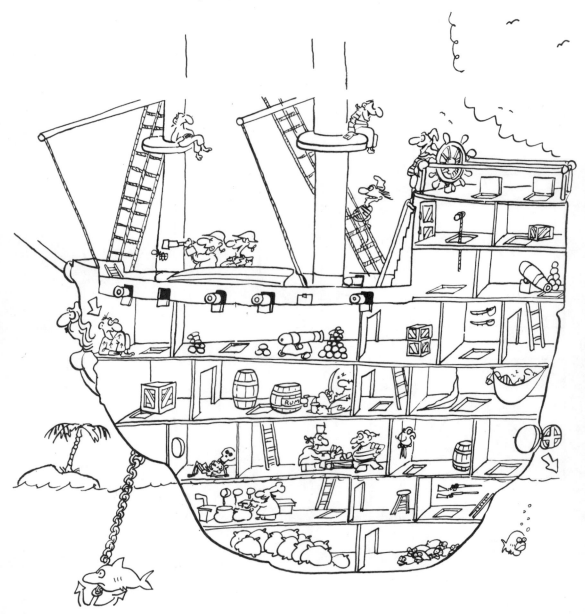

Go Fly a Kite

These four enthusiasts have managed to get their kite strings tangled. Whose kite is whose?

Solutions

Lowdown Logic I

1. None. No bird would stay after the first shot.

2. Take five sandwiches out of the bag and give one to each of five children. Then give the sixth child the bag containing the sandwich that is left.

3. Put three cakes into each of three bags then put these three bags into the fourth bag.

4. The day is Tuesday.

5. All of them.

6. The fishermen were a man, his son, and his grandson.

7. The heart was still only 1 m from the ground. A tree grows from the top not the base.

Leading Question

Of the four knots in Robert's lead only Nos 1 and 3 would not stay knotted.

Cut the Cube

There will be 8 cubes with 3 patterned faces each, 24 with 2 patterned faces, 24 with 1, 8 with none.

I'll Rephrase That

1. A square meal.

2. Plus-fours.

3. Space invaders.

4. A crooked deal.

5. Everything's coming up roses.

6. Down and out.

7. Beside myself.

8. Apple turnover.

9. Down under.

10. A fall in profits.

11. Going round in circles.

12. Upside-down cake.

13. Worn out.

14. Bottoms up.

15. Step by step.

Mirror Mirror

D is the correct mirror image.

Transformations

BLACK SLACK SHACK SHARK SHARE SHIRE SHINE WHINE WHITE.

Words Fail Me

1. Because a 'B' always comes after it.

2. The letter C.

3. A kitten.

4. No 'L' (Noel).

5. Because it is at the end of pork.

6. XTC (ecstasy).

7. NOON.

8. Neither. The yolk of an egg is yellow.

9. U and I.

10. Too wise you are, too wise you be, I see you are too wise for me.

11. The letter T.

12. "Madam, I'm Adam."

13. NME (enemy).

14. Jonah.

15. TDS (tedious).

16. KG (cagey).

17. We will allow B on E = bone, or BE low = below.

18. Barbara.

19. XMN (examine).

20. SPINACH (SP in a CH).

Something's Fishy!

1. A flying fish. **2.** An upstairs busdriver's cabin. **3.** An incomplete bicycle wheel. **4.** A half-price sale offering only a quarter off (25 per cent). **5.** Highly explosive milk. **6.** A square car wheel. **7.** A brick instead of a car wheel. **8.** A reader laughing at bad news. **9.** Ice cream cones from a hot dog stand. **10.** A three-armed woman. **11.** A fish being walked. **12.** Windswept hair and scarf going in opposite directions. **13.** A robber running **into** a bank. **14.** A dog with three hind legs. **15.** Cakes in the butcher shop window. **16.** Door with handle on same side as hinges. **17.** An upside down flower box. **18.** An unhappy baby in a "happy" baby advertisement. **19.** A fish perched on a roof.

Riddle-Me-Ree

1. In a draughts game.

2. An egg.

3. An umbrella.

4. Soap

5. The man's name was NOT.

6. A beard.

7. A shadow.

Imagine That!

Three pieces of paper in each case.

Diregrams

1. One route is as follows:
E — B — D — C — B — A — C — F — D — E — F

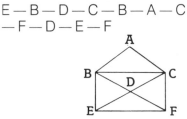

2. Here's where the hoops should fall.

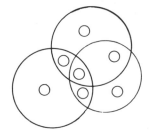

3. With C as the starting point here's a route to follow:
C — D — J — F — H — J — K — E — F — B — E — A — C — F — G — C

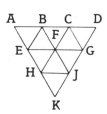

4. The trick is to fold the paper over. Then place the point of the pencil on the paper where the folded end meets it, draw the dot then move onto the folded-over portion. The going from here is easy.

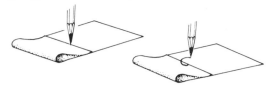

5. Try the following route: A to B; by upper curve to E; to D; by upper curve to C; straight line to D; by lower curve to C; straight line to B; by lower curve to E; to F.

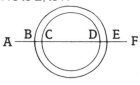

It's Dicey
B.

Sleeping on the Job
The distances are the same.

Oh No, Not Maths!

1. It will be a red odd number.

2. 66.

3. Sixteen.

4. The same number — that is 5 cats.

5. IV (ivy).

6. Six is three-quarters of 8 so including the big slice there are 9 slices of cake.

7. Take away the letter S(even).

8. The number 8. Take away the top half and 0 is left.

9. Twenty. You counted the same houses going and coming.

10. Neither is right.

11. Drop the letter S from SIX to obtain IX — the Roman number for nine.

12. Six matches.

13. A towel — sorry, we couldn't resist it.

14. Hiram I invented his square record in 1881. Hiram II invented the square harp in 1961.

15. Sixty-three jelly beans.

16. If you worked out that there were 6 sultanas and 6 soubrettes, bravo. But it was not necessary because if the mothers did not take part the work force is halved, thus the time taken would be 12 months.

17. Patrick is correct if you express the sum
$9 + 9 + 9 + 99 + 999 = 1125$.

18. How about $5/5 + 5 \times 5 + 5 = 31$?

19. O T T F F S S E N T
     N W
     E O
Now can you complete it?

Worth a Try?
Shirt fronts — No. 31. Shirt backs — No. 3.

Strange Relations

1. Margery was looking at a photograph of her father.

2. The two boys are triplets. Their sister goes to a ladies' college.

3. A step farther.

4. His sister.

5. Maxwell has four daughters and three sons.

6. Such a marriage would be impossible, for if there is a widow, there is no husband to marry.

7. The surgeon was the boy's mother.

8. Their middle name.

Which Map?
Shirl is the only correct mapper.

Card Trick
Ten of diamonds, king of hearts and 8 of spades.

How Many Triangles?
We stopped counting at 56.

Oddly Enough
All the drawings but No. 4 are facing out. The motor bike is seen from the side.

Lowdown Logic II

1. There are three children. A boy on the right, a girl in the middle and a girl on the left.

2. As only one is telling the truth try each in turn to see if it is possible for him or her to be telling the truth while the other two are lying.
You'll find that Bobby is the only possible culprit.

3. It's Friday.

4. Jessie has to pull three gloves out of the drawer to be sure of getting a pair.

5. The match.

Seeing Things
Both sunshade handles are the same length.

Coining It

1. Place the coin at the base of the cross on top of the coin at the middle of the cross.

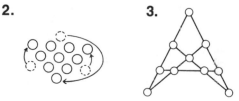

2.   **3.**

4. Remember that a coin has two faces so to the person rolling it leftward, the movement will appear to be anticlockwise. But to anyone opposite, it will be clockwise.

5. Move **Bb** to the right of **C.** Move **CB** to the vacant space, move **Aa** to the vacant space leaving **CBAab.**

Snails' Pace
The dotted lines are of equal length, so the snails will reach their destination at the same time.

The Animals Went in Two by Threes
Five animals.

How Many Squares?
There are 10 squares in the modern painting — 11 squares if you count the painting itself.

Match Magic

1. (a)   (b)

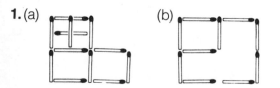

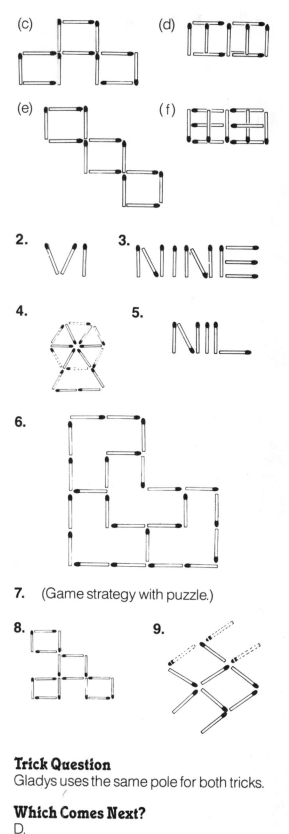

(c)   (d)

(e)   (f)

2. VI   **3.** NINE

4.   **5.** NIL

6.

7. (Game strategy with puzzle.)

8.   **9.**

Trick Question
Gladys uses the same pole for both tricks.

Which Comes Next?
D.

What's Odd?
All but D come in pairs.

Cross Words?

¹P	²U	³N	⁴C	⁵H
⁶P	U	N	C	H
⁷P	U	N	C	H
⁸P	U	N	C	H
⁹P	U	N	C	H

Lowdown Logic III

1. The error lies in the fact that the tenth man having taken possession of the ninth bed, the eleventh guest should occupy the tenth bed.

The man who is called from sharing the first bed is not the eleventh man, but the second man.

2. The date on the lamp could not be genuine, as nobody could anticipate an event by 108 years.

3. The men looked at each other. The first man saw that the other's face was dirty. Hence he assumed that his own was likewise.

The man with the dirty face saw the clean face of his companion and supposed that his own was likewise.

4. "Change horses."

5. The friend whom Duffy met must have been a lady — that is Margaret's mother. As Duffy had once known her very well, he would, of course, know her Christian name.

Doodlegrams

1. A giraffe passing a second-storey window.

2. A worm crawling over a razor blade.

3. Two elephants back to back.

4. A soldier and a dog going round a corner.

5. Two polar bears in a snowstorm.

6. A boat arriving too late to save a drowning witch.

7. A Mexican on a bicycle.

8. A woman scrubbing the floor.

9. An elephant sneezing.

10. A banana with glasses.

11. A stork with a wooden leg.

12. Snakes swallowing cricket balls.

13. The moon through a keyhole.

14. A worm that chased cars.

15. A bear climbing a pine tree.

Bound for Botany Bay

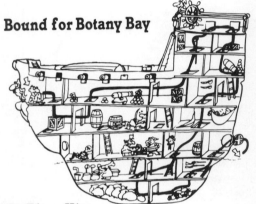

Go Fly a Kite
People and kites match as follows: 1B, 2D, 3C, 4A.

ANGUS & ROBERTSON PUBLISHERS

Unit 4, Eden Park, 31 Waterloo Road,
North Ryde, NSW, Australia 2113;
94 Newton Road, Auckland 1,
New Zealand; and
16 Golden Square, London W1R 4BN,
United Kingdom

First published in Australia
by Angus & Robertson Publishers in 1984
This new edition published in 1986
First published in the United Kingdom
by Angus & Robertson (UK) Ltd in 1986
Reprinted 1987, 1988, 1989

Copyright © text Angus & Robertson Publishers 1984, 1986
Copyright © illustrations Patrick Cook 1984

National Library of Australia
Cataloguing-in-publication data.

Brainteasers and puzzles for Kids.
ISBN 0 207 15227 6.

1. Puzzles — Juvenile literature. I. Cook, Patrick,
1949-

793.73

Typeset in Helvetica by The Type Shop
Printed in Hong Kong